SILLY STORIES

Kingfisher Books, Grisewood & Dempsey Ltd,
Elsley House, 24–30 Great Titchfield Street,
London W1P 7AD.

First published in 1988 by Kingfisher Books

BRITISH LIBRARY CATALOGUING IN PUBLICATION DATA
Rosen, Michael, *1946*–
    Silly stories.
    I. Title   II. Brown, Mik
    823'.914[J]
ISBN 0 86272 335 3

Phototypeset by Rowland Phototypesetting Ltd,
Bury St Edmunds, Suffolk
Printed in Spain

SILLY STORIES

By
Michael Rosen
Illustrated by
Mik Brown

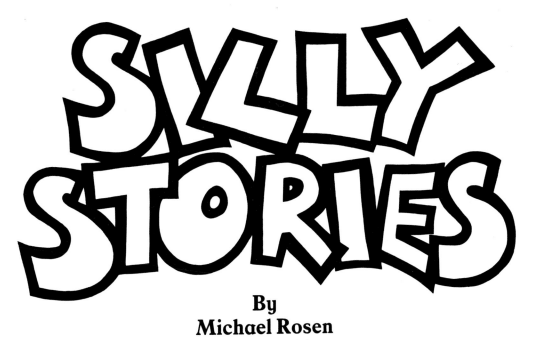

Kingfisher Books

4

A man went on holiday to Africa and bought a gorilla.
On the way back he was coming through customs
and he thought, 'Oh no, I'm never going to be able to
get through here, I know that you're not allowed to
bring gorillas in. I'll have to smuggle it in.'

So what he did was slap a thick slice of bread and
butter on both ears of the gorilla and he walked up to the
customs man.

The customs man went looking through all his suitcases
and bags, and then in the end he looked up and pointed
at the gorilla. "What's that?" he said.

The man got angry and said, "Look here, of
course you can go through my suitcases, but
what I put in my sandwiches is my
business, OK?"

"Mum, Mum," shouted Tom, "little Sally's broken my toy train."

"Now that's naughty, Sally," said Mum. "How did she do it, Tom?"

"She didn't duck when I hit her on the head with it," said Tom.

A posh man was waiting at the doctor's.
Opposite him was a small boy who kept
sniffing.

Sniff-sniff. Sniff. SNIFF.

In the end, the man couldn't stand it
any more. "Have you got a hankie?" he
said.

"Yeah," said the boy, "but I ain't
lending it to you."

There were these three children and they came to a magic slide. A little man was there and he said, "Whatever you shout as you're sliding down this slide you get as a present when you get to the bottom."

So the first kid slides down and he shouts, "G O L D" and he lands up in a great big pile of gold. The second kid slides down and he shouts, "D I A M O N D S" and he lands up in a great big pile of diamonds. And the third kid slides down and he shouts, "W E E E E E E E" and he lands up in a great big pool of . . .!

An inspector got on a bus and went up to the
top deck. He looked at a little girl's ticket
and said, "Excuse me, dear, where did you get
on?"

And the little girl said, "Downstairs."

9

There was this man, and he bought a horse and he jumped on it and said, "GIDDYUP!" But the horse wouldn't move. So he said, "How do you make this horse go?"

And the man selling the horse said, "You say, 'Thank goodness'."

"And how do you get it to stop?" said the man.

And the man selling the horse said, "You say, 'Bellybutton'."

So off went the man on the horse. But the horse started going faster and faster and faster and the man started getting scared and he knew where the horse was taking him – right up to the edge of a Huge Cliff! 'Oh no,' he thought, 'I've forgotten how to get the horse to stop. What am

I supposed to say? Ooooh, what is it?' And the
horse was getting nearer and nearer . . .
'What's the word? Oh no . . .' And the horse was
right up to the edge . . . and he remembered.
He shouted, "BELLYBUTTON!"
And the horse stopped.

"Phew," said the man. "Thank goodness." And
the horse went whoooosh, straight over the edge.

A boy went into a shop and said, "Can I have some cleaning fluid?"

The woman in the shop said, "Do you want a cleaner to put down the toilet, one that kills germs?"

The boy said, "Yes."

So the woman said, "I've got one here that kills very nearly all household germs." And she handed it to the boy.

It was in a bottle and next to it, stuck on with sellotape was a great big hammer. So the boy said, "What's the hammer for?"

And the woman said, "Well, I said that this cleaner kills nearly all household germs. Well, the hammer is so that you can hit the last few on the head."

Harry the poacher was out one night. He had in mind to steal a duck from the local pond for his Sunday dinner. He grabbed one, jumped into a hedge and started plucking its feathers off. All of a sudden he was surprised by the local policeman.

"Ah hah, it's you Harry, is it? Poaching again are you?"

"Oh no, officer," said Harry, "I'm only holding his clothes while he goes for a swim."

13

There was this group of people standing around with dogs when along came a little man with a funny looking yellow creature on a lead. There was another man there with a huge great big alsatian dog, and just for fun he let his alsatian dog off his lead and sent it off to scare the little man and his funny looking yellow animal.

Just as the big alsatian came up to the funny looking yellow animal, it lifted up its yellow head and with one great big bite bit off the alsatian dog's head.

14

The man who owned the alsatian said, "Oh no, what have you done? What sort of dog have you got there?"

The little man looked a bit sorry and said, "Well, actually it's not a dog. It's an alligator with its tail chopped off. I painted it yellow for a joke."

There was a phone call for the head teacher so she picked up the phone and she said, "Yes?"

And a voice said, "I'm terribly sorry, Darren Wilkins won't be at school today."

So the headmistress said, "Why not?"

And the voice said, "'Cos he's ill in bed."

So the headmistress said, "Oh dear, what a shame, and who's speaking please?"

And the voice said, "My Dad."

16

Two young men who wanted to look smart for going up town were checking each other's clothes over. One of them says to the other, "Your coat looks a right mess, you ought to use a coat hanger."

The next week when they met up, the one who had been wearing the untidy coat said, "I bought one of those coat hangers, but they don't half make your shoulders ache."

A man was going along in the desert in Australia when his car suddenly stopped. Nothing he could do would get it to go, so he got out and started to walk. He walked and he walked and he walked and soon he was feeling terribly, terribly thirsty. Finally he saw, coming into view, a little old shack by the side of the road. He staggered up to the door and shouted, "Water, water, water."

A man popped his head out the window and said, "Sorry pal, I only sell ties."

So the man walked on. And he walked and he walked and he walked and his mouth completely dried up. Then, coming into view, he saw another little old shack by the side of the road. He staggered up to the door and shouted, "Water, water, water."

A man popped his head out the window and said, "Sorry pal, I only sell ties."

So the man walked on. Finally he couldn't walk any more so he crawled.

He crawled and he crawled and he crawled till coming into view he saw a hotel. There by the side of the road, right in the middle of the desert, was the Hotel Splendid. And it was a really posh hotel with a man in uniform on the steps outside. The man crawled up to the steps and gasped, "At last, water, water, water."

And the man in uniform said, "Sorry pal, you can't come in here dressed like that, you're not wearing a tie."

The doctor called round at Mr Griffiths the farmer's house. At the door was Mr Griffiths' little girl, Rosie.

"Is your father in, Rosie?" said the doctor.

"No," said Rosie.

"Will he be back soon?" said the doctor.

"Oh yes," said Rosie, "he's in the pigsty, cleaning the pigs out. You'll see which one is father, he's got his hat on."

A man was sitting in a cafe having a drink when he called the waitress over. He pointed to his cup.

"This stuff tastes very funny. What do you call it? Coffee or tea?"

"What do you mean sir?" said the waitress.

"It tastes like paint," said the man.

"Ah well," said the waitress, "if it tastes like paint it must be coffee. Our tea tastes like soap."

A woman went to the dentist and the dentist had really bad eyesight. When the dentist had finished, he said, "Thank you very much, that's all for now Mrs Johnson."

And the woman said, "My name's not Johnson, it's Harvey. Remember, I'm Mrs Harvey, the one who came to see you about sore gums."

And the dentist said, "Sore gums? Sore gums? I'm not surprised you've got sore gums. I've just taken all your teeth out."

Dad was leaving to go to America. He had four minutes to catch his train to the airport. His family were all standing on the pavement saying goodbye to him when suddenly he couldn't find his air-ticket.

So he said to his son, "Dash back to the flat and see if I left the ticket up there." They live on the tenth floor . . . and the lift isn't working. The son dashes off. Three minutes later the boy is back, panting like he's run a marathon.

"Yes Dad," he says, "your ticket's on the table, right where you left it."

A man went into a police station one day, and said, "I want to complain. I've got three big brothers. We all live in one room. One of my brothers has got 17 cats. Another one has got 15 dogs. And the other one has got four goats and a pig. The smell in there is terrible. I want you to do something about it."

"Well, sir," said the policeman. "Has the room got any windows?"

"Yes, of course it has," said the man.

"Well, sir," said the policeman. "Open them."

"Don't be daft," said the man. "I'd lose all my pigeons."

A little girl hurt her hand when she fell over on her rollerskates so she went to see the doctor. "Do you think I'll ever be able to play the piano?" she said.

"Oh yes, dear, of course," said the doctor kindly. "In just a few weeks time you'll be able to play the piano all right."

"That's amazing," said the girl, "because I couldn't play it before."

A teacher asked the class if anything funny had happened to anyone that week. One girl told this story:

We have mice at home and our cat is too lazy to catch them. One morning we got up and there were three of them dancing round the kitchen floor. It made my Mum late for work and she dashed out the house. On the way to the station she went past a shop that sells mousetraps. She rushed in and said, "Quick, I want a mousetrap. Hurry up, give it to me fast, I've got to catch a train."

And the man in the shop said, "Sorry madam, we haven't got any that big."

Everyone was in the classroom when the teacher said, "Where's your pencil, Maggie?"

"Ain't got one, miss," said Maggie.

And the teacher said, "How many times have I told you not to say, 'ain't got one'. Listen: I haven't got one. You haven't got one. We haven't got one. They haven't got one. Now do you understand?"

And Maggie said, "Well, where are all the pencils if nobody ain't got none?"

Mrs Rossiter hadn't paid the electricity bill. She kept getting letters asking her to pay and she didn't answer any of them, until in the end, the electricity people sent a man over to cut off the electricity. Mrs Rossiter saw him coming, told her son, Mike, to answer the door and rushed off and hid behind the curtain. Mike answered the door.

"Where's your mother?" said the electricity man.

"She's out," said Mike.

"Oh is she?" said the man, looking at the bottom of the curtain. "Does she always go out without her feet on?"

A boy was coming out of school when suddenly he saw an elephant. It walked up to a jeweller's shop on the corner, smashed the window and started sucking jewels up its trunk. After it had taken all the rings, gold watches and bracelets, it turned round and made off in the direction of the zoo.

The boy, who was called Joe, rushed off to the police station to tell them about it. The policeman on duty took down everything that Joe told him and then said, "Now, lad, was this elephant an African or an Indian elephant?"

"I don't know where it came from," said Joe.

"Well, lad," said the policeman, "the African elephant has big ears and the Indian elephant has small ears. What kind was this one?"

"I don't know, sir," said Joe. "This one had a stocking over its head."

A girl was asking her Dad a few things:

Dad, how do you spell Venezuela?

I don't know, love.

Dad, what's the name of the president of France?

I don't know, love.

Dad, what's the longest river in the world?

I don't know, love.

Dad, you don't mind me asking you all these questions, do you?

Course I don't, love. Asking questions is how you learn things.